The Novello Prima...
ea
gospels

Novello Publishing Limited
part of The Music Sales Group

London / New York / Paris / Sydney / Copenhagen / Berlin / Madrid / Tokyo

Published by
Novello Publishing Limited
14/15 Berners Street, London, W1T 3LJ, England.

Exclusive distributors:
Music Sales Limited
Distribution Centre, Newmarket Road, Bury St Edmunds, Suffolk, IP33 3YB.

Music Sales Pty Limited
20 Resolution Drive, Caringbah, NSW 2229, Australia.

Order No. NOV170566
ISBN 1-84449-596-5
This collection © Copyright 2004 Novello & Company Limited.

Music engraved by Note-orious Productions Limited.
Cover designed by Miranda Harvey.
Arranged by Rick Hein.
Compiled and edited by Heather Ramage.
Printed in the United Kingdom.

www.musicsales.com

Amazing Grace

Words by John Newton
Music: Traditional

6

8

9

Go Down Moses

Traditional

13

15

Go Tell It On The Mountain

Traditional/Heumann

Joshua Fought The Battle Of Jericho

Traditional

26

37 Em B⁷ Em B⁷ Em B⁷

Trum - pet - ers, let 'em wail!"__ Josh- ua said, "Now

trum - pets be- gan to sound; Josh- ua com- mand- ed the

40 Em Am B⁷

chil - dren shout!"___ and the walls came a - tum - bl - ing

chil - dren to shout,___ and the walls came a - tum - bl - ing

42 Em *mp*

down. Josh-u - a__ fought the bat-tle of Je - ri - cho,

mp

down. Josh-u - a__ fought the bat-tle of Je - ri - cho,

melody

mf

29

battle of Jericho, battle of Jericho,

battle of Jericho, battle of Jericho,

Josh - u - a___ fought the bat - tle of Je - ri - cho

Josh - u - a___ fought the bat - tle of Je - ri - cho

walls came tumb - ling down. Josh - ua fought the bat - tle of___

walls came tumb - ling down. Josh - ua fought the bat - tle of___

Steal Away

Traditional

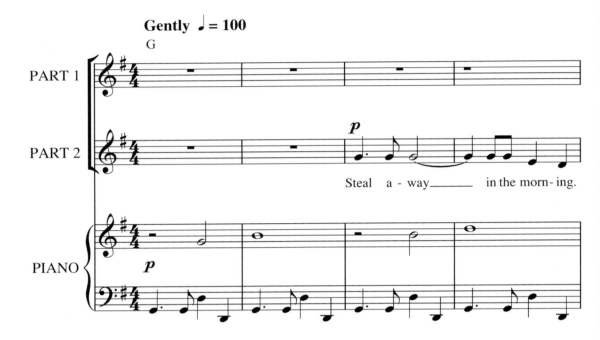

34

Swing Low, Sweet Chariot

Traditional

39

When The Saints Go Marching In

Traditional

The Gospel Train
(Get On Board Little Children)

Traditional

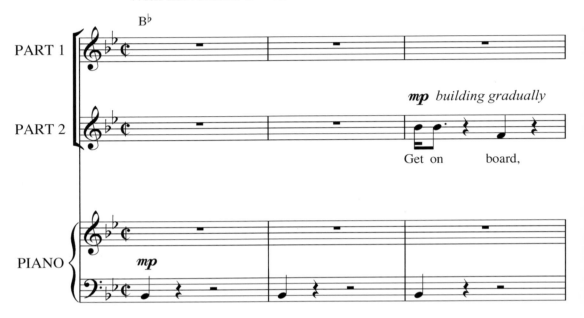

To ⊕ CODA

Get on board gos-pel train's a com - in'.

gos-pel train's a-com - in. I

Lis - ten,___ train's a com - in',___

hear the train's a-com - in',___ she's com - in' 'round the curve,___

train's a - com - in',_____ com - in'

_____ she's loos-en'd all her steam___ and brakes,___ and

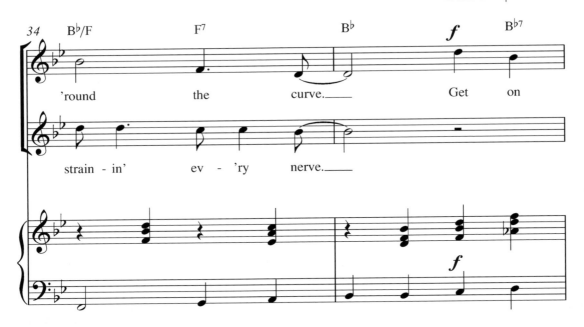

⊕ **CODA**